ROSANNE KELLER

LifeStories 2

New Readers Press

LifeStories 2
1-56420-403-0

Copyright © 2003 New Readers Press
New Readers Press
Division of ProLiteracy Worldwide
1320 Jamesville Avenue, Syracuse, New York 13210
www.newreaderspress.com

Printed in the United States of America
9   8   7   6   5   4   3   2

All proceeds from the sale of New Readers Press materials
support literacy programs in the United States and worldwide.

Acquisitions Editor: Paula Schlusberg
Content Editor: Terrie Lipke
Copy Editor: Marcia Hough
Production Director: Heather Witt
Designer: Kimbrly Koennecke
Illustrations: Linda Tiff
Production Specialist: Jeffrey R. Smith
Cover Design: Andrea Woodbury

Contents

Finding a Job

Joon is sitting quietly at the kitchen table. Kim pours some coffee for Joon. She asks him, "How is your job search going?"

Joon says, "I looked on the bulletin board at the supermarket. I found two jobs that are interesting. I called about them. Now I have two interviews today."

Kim says, "That's great! Why do you look so sad?"

Joon answers, "I'm not sad. I'm worried! I really want to get a job today."

"Don't worry," says Kim. "You have to keep trying. Maybe you won't get a job today. But you can try again tomorrow."

Ready for Interviews

Joon walks out of the bedroom. He is dressed for his interviews. He is wearing a sport coat and dress pants.

Kim says, "You look ready for your interviews. I would hire you!"

Joon says, "Thanks, but I feel very nervous."

Kim says, "Don't be nervous, Joon. It is just questions and answers. They ask questions. And you answer. Then you ask questions. And they answer."

Joon says, "I can ask them how much they pay. And do I have to wear a uniform? What are the hours? Do I get paid more for overtime? Do they have a health plan? How much vacation time do I get?"

"Slow down!" says Kim. "Let them ask questions first. Just relax. And be polite. You'll do fine. Good luck, Joon!"

Joon's Good News

Kim comes home from her job at Pizza Time. She sits down to rest her feet.

Joon walks in the door. He takes off his coat. He says, "I'm glad I don't have to wear a suit to work!"

Kim jumps up from her chair. "To work?" she asks. "Did you get a job?"

Joon looks at her and smiles proudly. "I will be a machine operator at Seacoast Industries. I start next Monday."

Joon hugs Kim. Then he says, "I'll tell you about it during dinner. I'm taking you and Han out to eat!"

Kim says, "That's a great idea. Can we go to a place that does not serve pizza?" Kim and Joon laugh.

New Job, New Problems

The Lee family ate at a Tex-Mex restaurant. They talked about the things they could do now that Joon had a job.

Then Kim said to Joon, "I'm glad our problems are over. I have some news, too. We are going to have a baby!"

Joon hugged his wife. He said, "This is the best news! I am so happy."

Han said, "I will be a big brother!"

Then Kim asked, "Joon, what hours do you work?"

Joon smiled proudly. "My shift starts at 4 P.M. I have to catch the bus at 3:30 so I can get there on time."

Kim shook her head. "Then you won't get home until after midnight," she said. "Joon, we have a problem."

Joon said, "Oh, no. A new problem?"

"Yes," Kim said, "During the week, I work from 10:30 A.M. to 4:30 P.M. I get home at 5:15. Then I cook dinner for you and Han. You are home with Han after school every day. Now who will be home with Han?"

Joon said, "I was so glad to get this job. I didn't think of that. What can we do?"

Kim started to cry. She said, "I don't know. What about child care?"

Then Joon smiled. "I have an idea. Child care is expensive. So, you could ask your boss to schedule you fewer hours. Then you can be there when Han comes home from school."

"When will we see you?" Kim asked.

Joon replied, "Kim, we're building our future. Now, you should be there for Han. You can cut your hours. And then you can take better care of yourself and our new baby. We will have family time on the weekends."

Kim said, "You're right, Joon. We need to make the most of our time together. And we can look forward to a great future."

Small Talk

One Sunday, Joon took Han to the baseball game. It was sunny and warm. But in the sixth inning, it started to rain. Han and Joon walked home in the rain. On the way home they stopped for ice cream. They had a fun day.

On Monday, at work, Joon listened to some men talking. They talked about the weather and about the ball game. They talked about what they had for lunch. It was all small talk.

"Hey, Joon," said Ramon. Ramon was Joon's supervisor. "What did you do this weekend?"

Joon said, "I took Han to the ball game."

Ramon said, "I remember when my son was little. We had a lot of fun together." Ramon looked at Joon. "Children grow up very fast."

Then Joon and Ramon talked about their own fathers. Joon told Ramon about growing up in Korea. And Ramon talked about his own family.

Afterward, Joon thought this did not seem like small talk. Joon felt like he and Ramon were becoming friends.

Need and Want

Han said, "I *need* a bicycle. I *need* one!"

His mother said, "No, Han, you don't *need* a bike. You *want* a bike. There is a difference between *need* and *want*." She pointed to the sink. "I *need* a new dish pan. But I *want* a dishwasher."

Han smiled, "I want a dog. But I need a new notebook."

Joon joined in. "I want a car. No! We *need* a car. Our family is growing. We can all get around easier in a car. My bus pass costs $50 a month. If I saved $50 every month for a year, I'd have $600. That could be a down payment on a used car."

Kim said, "How would you get to work if you didn't ride the bus?"

Joon laughed. He said, "I'd ride Han's bike."

New Bikes

Joon and Han walked to the park on Saturday. Kim went shopping. She put a bike on layaway for Han. She couldn't wait to tell Joon about it. If she paid $20 each month, it would be paid for by Christmas. That would make Han so happy. Kim smiled all the way home.

Soon after Kim got home, the door flew open. Han ran into the room shouting, "Mom! Mom! I have a new bike!" Joon rolled the bike into the living room.

Kim looked at Joon. She was shocked. They couldn't afford to buy a new bicycle.

Later, Kim asked Joon, "Where did you get that bike? And how did you pay for it?" Kim felt angry and worried. "You didn't use a credit card, did you? Or our savings?"

Joon said, "Don't worry, Kim. The bike is not new. It is a used bike. I bought it from Ramon for only $15. He said it used to be his son's bike. But Ramon's son is grown up now. Each day on my break I worked on it. I took it apart and carefully cleaned and oiled it. Then Ramon helped me paint it." Joon looked proud. "And you thought it was new!"

Kim told Joon about the layaway. She said, "I will go and tell them I don't want the new bike. I can ask for a refund."

Joon said, "I have another surprise, Kim. Ramon had two other old bikes—adult size. I am going to fix them up for us. In a few weeks, the whole Lee family will have wheels!"

Kim said, "Joon, I am happy we have a way to buy bikes. But I don't know how to ride a bicycle. What if I can't do it?"

"Don't worry, I'll teach you," Joon said. He grinned. "On weekends, we can go on family bike rides."

Driving Practice

Johnny was very excited. Finally, he was ready to get his driver's license. He was so proud to have his learner's permit. He carried his driver's manual like a prize.

That night Johnny opened his driver's manual to study. He thought this would be easy. But it was not easy. It was hard to read. There were so many things to remember.

Even the traffic signs were confusing. They were all different shapes and colors. There were triangles, rectangles, circles, octagons, and diamonds. Johnny was worried. What if he couldn't remember all this on the test?

The next day, Johnny's father, Tony, took him to an empty parking lot to practice driving. His father told him what to do. He said, "Slow down. Stop here. Not so fast. Take it easy. Look around. Don't play the radio. Look in the rearview mirror. Stop!" Johnny stopped the car. He looked confused. Tony said, "Son, good driving takes practice."

Johnny practiced a lot in the next few weeks. Then Tony took Johnny to the Department of Motor Vehicles for the tests. Johnny passed the written test and the road test. Johnny showed his father his new temporary driver's license. Johnny beamed with pride.

When it was time to go home, Tony got in the driver's seat. Johnny's proud smile faded. He was angry. Driving home, Tony turned to Johnny. "I'm really proud of you, son. But you need more practice before. . . ."

Suddenly they heard a siren. Red lights were flashing in the rearview mirror. Johnny's father pulled the car over to the curb and stopped. A police officer came up to the window. Johnny turned away to hide his smile.

The police officer wrote Tony a ticket for speeding. Tony waited silently. He looked embarrassed. After the officer left, Tony was still quiet. Johnny turned to him. "Can I practice now, Dad?" he asked.

Sign of Growing Up

One day, after school, Tony told Johnny he could take the car. "But be careful," Tony said. "And don't speed."

Johnny was excited. "All right! I'm going to pick up Sam and Carlos and Rosa and. . . ."

Tony interrupted him. "Wait a minute! You are still a new driver. I don't want you to have more than one passenger. You must not get distracted."

Then Aunt Tessa joined in. "Don't stay out late. And don't go too far," she said.

"Call us if you get in trouble," Tony said.

Johnny looked at his father and his aunt and said, "I'm only going to get a hamburger. Don't you trust me?"

Johnny's aunt looked at him. "He's right, Tony. Johnny is growing up. He has a license now. We need to trust him more."

"You'll see," Johnny said. "I will drive safely. I'll show you that you can trust me."

Women's Day

One day Olga was reading the newspaper. She saw an ad for an art show at the museum. It was called, "Women's Art—Works by Women from Around the World."

I'd like to go to that, she thought. I wonder if anyone would like to go with me? I know. I will call some of the women I know. I'll call Isabel, Kim, Helen, and Althea. I'll ask if they would like to go.

Olga went to the phone. She called Isabel. "Would you like to join me for an outing next Saturday?" she asked. Olga told Isabel about the show.

Isabel said, "That sounds very interesting. I would love to come with you."

Olga called Kim Lee. Kim said she would also like to come.

Olga asked, "And how about Joon? Would he like to come, too?"

Kim laughed. "I don't think Joon would be interested in a women's art show. Besides, he likes to spend time with Han on the weekends. They are probably going to a ball game."

Then Olga talked with Helen and Althea. Helen said she was sorry she couldn't come. She had other plans. But Althea was excited about going. So Olga asked if Monroe would like to come along.

"Oh, I don't think so," Althea said. "He doesn't enjoy museums. We went to the history museum once, and he couldn't wait to leave. Besides, it will be fun to spend the afternoon with my women friends."

Olga said, "That's wonderful. We'll have a women's day out. Let's meet for lunch at that little café downtown."

After the Art Show

Kim and Althea walked to the bus stop together. They were laughing and talking.

"Wasn't that a wonderful art show?" Kim said. "I can't decide which painting was my favorite."

Althea said, "My favorite was the painting of African women. Do you remember the one? They were sitting around a well. They were wearing such colorful clothes."

Kim said, "I enjoyed the photo of the young Chinese woman holding her newborn twins. The picture showed so much emotion. She looked happy, scared, and tired all at once."

"And I liked the carving of the old Mexican woman," Althea said. "She looked very strong and wise."

"You know," Kim said. "I think the best part of the day was lunch. It was great to just sit and talk. Don't you like Olga? She is a very wise lady, too."

Althea smiled. "She may be older than we are, but she sure is fun. I want to get to know her better."

Kim nodded. "I do, too," she said.

"I think we should do this more often," Althea said. "Let's see if we can find another event to attend."

Kim stopped. "Yes," she said. "That's a good idea. But we don't need to wait for a special event. We can make any day special just by getting together."

"You're right," Althea said.

Past and Present

"Watch me, Dad," Han yelled. "Watch how fast I can go!"

"I'm watching," Joon said. He watched Han ride his new bike down the street. But in his mind, Joon was remembering when he was the boy on the bike. "Time to come in," Joon shouted to Han. But Han was heading around the corner.

"Han," Joon said later. "I called you, and you did not come in the house. When I call, I expect you to listen."

Han said, "I'm sorry. I didn't hear you."

Joon sat down next to Han. "Each day I watch you grow. I watch you paint pictures in your room. I watch you ride your bike. I watch you work on your lessons. I see you study hard." Joon hugged Han. "I am very proud of you."

"What were you like when you were a boy?" Han asked.

"Things were different then," Joon said. "When I was a boy, I worked with my father at his shop. I studied hard, too. And as I got older, I looked forward to having my own family."

"Now you have me," said Han.

"That's right," Joon said. "And I want you to have a good life. You will grow up very fast. When you are a man, I want you to be proud and happy. I am very proud of you. I want you to be proud of yourself, too. And I want you to always be as happy as you are now."

Joon hugged Han. "And Han," he said, "some things have not changed. When I was your age, I didn't always come in when I was called either."

Han smiled up at his father.

Understanding English

Kim said, "English is crazy. You learn a verb. Then you learn to add '*ed*' to make the verb past tense. That sounds easy." Kim shook her head. "Then you learn that there are many verbs that change completely in the past tense! *Be* becomes *was*. *Do* becomes *did*. And can you believe that *buy* becomes *bought*?"

Joon said, "How about *speak* and *spoke*? I spoke to you about this last week. But I will speak to you about it again now." He laughed. "Did you see the seesaw? I saw the seesaw. Han was playing on the seesaw. Then he slid down the slide. He is sliding down the slide right now."

Kim laughed. Then she looked very serious. "I will never understand this language," she said, sadly.

"You just have to memorize some things," Joon told her. "English is a language that does not always follow the rules. There is an exception to every rule." He reached for Kim's hand. "I would help you if I could. But I can't."

Kim said, "You *can't* or you *won't?*" She sighed. "Oh, this is so confusing. How will I ever learn?"

"Someone once told me that you need to keep trying," said Joon. "There is always tomorrow!"

"That sounds like good advice," said Kim, giggling.

"Just keep trying, Kim. Read English. Listen to English. Write English. Speak English. Think English. Breathe English." Joon took a deep breath. "We will make a rule. We will speak English at home every day." Then he smiled. "But, at night, when we're asleep?"

"We should dream in English!" Kim announced.

Cool Clothes

Althea, Monroe, and Jody were at the Dandelion Shop. They were going to the cashier to pay for Jody's dress.

"OK, Mom," Jody said. "I've got a new dress for the wedding. Now can I get something else? I want something new to wear to Karen's birthday party. Please?"

"Do you want another dress?" asked Althea.

"Mom!" Jody cried. "I can't wear a dress to the party! My friends will be wearing cool clothes."

Althea looked at her daughter. Jody was only 10 years old, but she knew what she wanted. "What do your friends wear to parties?" Althea asked her.

Jody ran to the children's department. "Let me show you," Jody said. "I want these." She pulled out a pair of faded jeans. "My friends all have pants like these."

"But they look old and worn out," Althea said. "Wouldn't you rather have these nice dark blue pants?"

"No, they look too new. People would make fun of me if I wore them," Jody said. "Mom, look at this T-shirt. This is just what I need to go with my new jeans." Jody pointed to a T-shirt with a picture of a rock band on it.

"Jody, that shirt is not pretty," Althea said. "I don't like it at all."

"I like it," Jody said. "This is what the cool kids wear."

"We'll get you jeans and a T-shirt if that is what you want," Althea told Jody. "But we need to agree on a pair of nice-looking jeans. And you need to find a T-shirt that I like, too."

Jody frowned. "Oh, Mom," she said. "If I can't have these clothes, can I at least get my ears pierced?"

Just Married

Althea, Monroe, and Jody walked up the church steps. They were all dressed up in their new clothes. The church was decorated with flowers and ribbons. "Oh, Mom, it is so beautiful," Jody said.

Soon the music began. The groom and his best man stood in the front of the church. The bride started walking toward him. "Why are you crying, Mom?" Jody asked.

"Memories," Althea whispered. She hugged Jody. "And thinking of the day when you will be a bride."

"Yuck," said Jody. Monroe just smiled.

After the wedding everyone went to the reception in the church basement. It was a big party. Everyone was drinking punch and dancing.

The bride and groom cut a big wedding cake. A photographer took their picture. Jody ate two pieces of cake. Then the bride and groom disappeared. "Where did they go?" Jody asked.

"They went to change their clothes so they can leave for their honeymoon," Althea told her. "The newlyweds are driving to Mexico for their honeymoon."

The wedding guests lined up outside the church. Each person had a handful of rice to throw on the newlyweds. "The rice is for good luck," Monroe said to Jody. A sign on the back of the newlyweds' car read, "Just Married."

Suddenly the bride and groom came out of the church door. They had on faded jeans and rock band T-shirts.

"Oh, this is so cool!" said Jody. "I can't wait to get married."

Learning to Relax

Olga felt so much better since she stopped smoking and lost a little weight. But still something wasn't right. The doctor told her she needed to reduce stress. He said she needed to worry less and learn to relax.

Olga invited Isabel and Helen for dinner. After they ate, the women sat and talked. Olga said, "I need some advice. My doctor wants me to relax and stop worrying about everything. Now I am worried because I don't know how to stop worrying!"

"Sometimes I have a hard time relaxing after work," said Isabel. "So I put on some pretty music and play solitaire or read. Why don't you try it?"

Olga turned on her stereo. Isabel chose a CD. Soothing music flowed into the room. "Now, what games do you know?" asked Helen.

"I can play solitaire, too," answered Olga.

Isabel said, "That's a great idea when you're alone. But since we are here tonight, let's play a board game."

The women listened to music, played a game, and laughed a lot. Olga was very relaxed.

On Saturday, Olga invited Althea to go for a walk. She told Althea about her evening with Helen and Isabel. "It's fun finding new ways to relax," Olga said. "I think spending time with my friends is very good for my health."

Althea asked, "Would you like to know what I do to relax?" Olga nodded. "I treat myself to a bubble bath. You should try it tonight! Light some scented candles, fill the tub, and add your favorite bath oil. Then just lie back and enjoy."

"That sounds like the perfect way to end a stressful day," Olga said. "Maybe you could help me shop for some candles and bath oil. My doctor will be very pleased when he sees how relaxed I am now."

It's Time!

Kim was 20 minutes late for work at Pizza Time. When she got there, Tony asked, "Is everything all right?"

"I'm not sure," Kim said. "I feel anxious today, but I don't know why."

Kim had always been very fast, neat, and organized. She could wait on six tables at once.

But today she couldn't keep the orders straight. She dropped things. She forgot to check on the customers. Finally Tony said, "Kim, I think you should go home early. Get some rest."

"Oh, thank you, Tony," Kim said. When she left, she forgot her coat.

That night when Joon came home, Kim was already in bed. Joon took off his coat. He was tired. He tiptoed into the bedroom. It felt so good to lie down.

In his dream Joon heard Kim calling. "It's time! It's time!" Joon opened his eyes. Kim was getting dressed. "I need to get to the hospital," she said.

Joon jumped out of bed. He threw on his clothes. He called a taxi. "We'll take Han to Tony's on the way," he said. Kim picked up her suitcase. "No!" Joon yelled. "Don't lift that! I'll carry it. I'll get Han, too. Sit down. What else can I do?"

Kim said, "Calm down, Joon. I'm fine. Everything will be OK."

At 8 A.M., Joon saw his daughter, Monica, for the first time. She was lying in Kim's arms. Joon put his arm around Kim and his daughter. "This is the third best day of my life," he said.

"What were the other two?" Kim asked.

"The first was the day we were married," Joon said. "The second was the day Han was born. And now this." Joon held Kim close. "I am happier than I ever thought I'd be. I have you and Han and Monica."

Han's Little Sister

It was 2:00 in the morning. Everything was quiet. Everything except Monica. Monica had been crying for hours. Kim was so tired. She fed the baby, changed the baby, and held the baby. But the baby still cried.

Finally Joon said, "Go to sleep, Kim. I will go and rock Monica."

Joon sat in the rocking chair. He held his tiny daughter close. He rocked and rocked. Monica kept crying.

"Life is hard, little daughter," Joon said to Monica. "But I will always be here for you." Joon reached over and turned on the CD player. Soft Korean music began to fill the room. "This is our music, Monica. This music is from my native country. It is your music, too."

But Monica would not stop crying. Joon sat rocking and thinking. Today he talked with Han's teacher, Ms. Hunter. She said Han is having a hard time adjusting to his sister. Joon smiled. Having a baby is a big adjustment for the whole family.

Joon heard the door open. Han came into the room. He was rubbing his eyes. "I can't sleep," he said. "What is wrong with Monica?"

"I don't know," Joon said. "Maybe she is having trouble sleeping, too." Han looked at his father rocking the new baby.

"Come here, Han," said Joon. "There is room for both of you in my lap."

Han crawled into Joon's lap. He leaned back against his father. And Joon put Monica in Han's arms. She was soft and warm. She snuggled close to Han's chest. Then she closed her eyes and fell asleep.

"Well, look at that," said Joon. "All she needed was her big brother." He rocked slowly in the big chair. "She will learn to depend on you. You two will help each other."

Han looked down at his baby sister. Then he whispered, "Look, Dad, she's smiling."

American Dream

Isabel likes Stefan very much. She likes to talk with him. She enjoys being with him when he is not working or going to school. Stefan has been taking night courses. He wants to be an electrician.

Isabel has big plans, too. She wants to be a teacher. That will take at least four years at the university. Right now, Isabel and Stefan are studying to become American citizens. After Isabel gets her citizenship, she will apply to college.

Stefan's citizenship interview is next month. After he becomes a citizen, he wants to travel. Stefan wants to drive all over the U.S. He is saving for the trip by putting aside money from every paycheck. Stefan used some of the money he saved to buy a used pickup truck and some camping equipment.

Isabel was just leaving the restaurant after work. She walked outside and a loud horn startled her. Stefan waved. "Hi, Isabel," he hollered.

"Where did you get that truck?" asked Isabel.

"Do you like it?" Stefan asked. "I've been saving up for it. Jump in, and I'll take you for a ride."

As they drove around in the truck, Stefan told Isabel about his dream trip. "I want to see all the sights from the Grand Canyon to Niagara Falls. And I want to go to Washington, D.C., and visit the places I learned about in citizenship class. Look on the map in the glove compartment."

Isabel opened up the map of the U.S. Many places were circled in red. "Wow!" said Isabel. "The trip sounds so exciting. I wish I could go."

"You could," said Stefan. "We could go together. It could be our honeymoon."

It took a minute for Isabel to realize what Stefan was saying. And when she did, she looked at him and smiled. Then she pointed to California on the map and said, "This is where our adventure will start."

Being American

Isabel looked around at the people in her citizenship class. It reminded her of the United Nations. There were people from all over the world. And they all wanted to become American citizens.

When Isabel first came to the U.S., she wasn't sure she would stay here. She was homesick. She missed her family. But finally she decided. And now, one day soon, she would become American.

As that day approached, Isabel wondered if that was the right decision. How would she feel after she took the oath? She felt guilty about leaving her native country. What about her own heritage? Her own culture? What about the relatives she still had in El Salvador? When she became an American citizen, would they still be her family? Would other people accept her as American? Isabel needed to talk to someone about her feelings.

After class, Isabel called Olga. "I want to ask you something," Isabel said. Olga invited her over for coffee.

Isabel sat down with her coffee cup. Olga brought each of them a piece of pie to go with their coffee.

Isabel looked at Olga. "Tonight I'm feeling a little homesick, I guess." She tore her napkin into little pieces as she talked. "I remember when I was a child in El Salvador. I remember the food my mother cooked. I remember my grandmother and grandfather and their old-fashioned ways."

Olga stirred her coffee. She didn't speak even when Isabel stopped to think.

"Sometimes I wonder if I should just go back," said Isabel. "It took me so long to decide to stay here. Then I thought about becoming a U.S. citizen. It took me even longer to decide what to do." She hadn't touched her coffee or pie. "Why am I suddenly not sure?"

Olga finally spoke. "You will never forget who you are or where you come from," she said. "El Salvador will always be a big part of your life. Becoming American does not mean you are giving up part of yourself. No. It means adding U.S. citizenship to your Salvadoran heritage." Olga smiled. She knew from her own experience that this was the truth.

"But will I really become American?" Isabel asked. "Or will I only have a paper that says I'm American?"

"Isabel, America is a place where all different cultures, traditions, and nationalities come together. That's why it's sometimes called a 'melting pot.' But I believe America is like a quilt with pieces of different colors and textures sewn together into a beautiful design. And the design is always growing and changing."

"But do *I* have to change to become a part of that?" Isabel asked.

"Change? We all change," Olga answered. "You have just taken many courses to get ready for citizenship. Education changes us. We learn and grow. We see things differently. I still eat Hungarian food. I still love Hungarian music. I still enjoy speaking Hungarian to my relatives and old friends. But I am American through and through."

"How do you know for sure?" Isabel asked.

Olga said, "Look at the pie we are eating with our coffee. It is apple pie." Olga laughed. "Haven't you heard the saying, 'American as apple pie'? Even our taste is American now."

Isabel laughed, too. "American as apple pie," she said. "I guess you're right. I make different choices without even thinking about them." Then she laughed again. "Did I tell you that Stefan and I are going to drive across the country to Niagara Falls? We even chose an American honeymoon!"

Gone Fishing

It was still dark when Joon got out of bed. He was very quiet. He didn't want to wake the children. He tiptoed to the living room where his fishing gear was all laid out.

Kim came out of the bedroom yawning. She made tea and cooked breakfast for Joon. "I hope you catch a big fish," she said. "Fresh fish for dinner would be wonderful."

Joon smiled. "I'll try. I've never been fishing in America. But Tony and Monroe say they know a good place." Joon thought back to his childhood in Korea. "I remember bringing home fresh fish for dinner. My mother was always glad when I didn't come home empty-handed."

Joon went outside. A few minutes later, he saw Tony's car coming up the street. Monroe was in the front seat. "It looks like a good day for fishing," Joon said. "I'm glad we're getting an early start. The fish are hungry in the morning." As they drove out of town, Joon watched out the window. He didn't see a lake.

Tony turned in front of a restaurant and parked the car. There still was no lake nearby. Tony and Monroe got out of the car. Joon didn't know why they were at a restaurant. But he got out, too.

"Come on," said Tony. "Let's eat." Inside the restaurant, Tony and Monroe ordered pancakes and eggs and bacon.

Joon ordered some tea. "I already ate," he said.

"You have?" questioned Monroe. "I'd never wake Althea this early. If I did, I'd be in big trouble."

"She wouldn't make breakfast for you?" asked Joon.

"Oh, sure. She'd make breakfast," said Monroe. He laughed. "Then she'd give me a list of things to do. Clean the garage, mow the lawn . . . I'd never get out of there!"

Tony laughed. But Joon was puzzled.

After breakfast, Tony drove a few miles to Al's Bait Shop. The three men went inside.

"Hi, Al," said Tony to the man in the store.

Al stood up from his chair. He said, "Hey, Tony. It's good to see you again. Sit down and have some coffee."

Tony introduced Joon and Monroe. Then they all sat down. Al handed each man a mug of coffee. "How are the fish biting these days?" asked Tony.

"Pretty good, I guess," Al said. Then he added, "But you have to put your hook in the water to catch one!" The men laughed.

Joon was confused. Of course you have to put your hook in the water if you're fishing. He looked out the window. He could finally see the lake. But now it was late in the morning. Why weren't they on the water?

Al and Tony and Monroe talked and talked. They talked about football, about the weather, about the news. Finally, they all went outside, and Al showed them a boat to rent for the day. It was just the right size. The men bought bait and loaded the boat.

Out on the water, Joon baited his hook. Monroe opened the cooler and took out a can of soda. Tony stopped the engine of the boat. He threw in the anchor. Then he also got a drink out of the cooler.

"This looks like a good place," he said. He leaned back and closed his eyes. "That sun sure does feel good."

Then Tony said, "I never did like to fish. But I love being out here, away from it all."

Monroe laughed. "I don't mind catching fish. I just don't like to clean them. And Althea would kill me if I brought any fish home for her to clean. That's why I just throw them back."

Joon felt a tug on his line and pulled in a very nice lake trout. Tony hadn't even baited a hook.

"Are you going to keep that one?" Monroe asked.

Joon said, "Of course. Kim is expecting me to bring home fresh fish for dinner."

Tony and Monroe looked at each other. "Well, I guess Kim is not like my wife," Monroe said. The men laughed.

Joon had caught three fish when Monroe said, "I'm getting hungry. Why don't we go back and get some lunch? Then I'd better go home. Althea wants me to mow the lawn."

When Joon got home, Kim said, "You are home early. Did you catch any fish?"

"I caught three fish," Joon replied. "And I learned that going fishing is not always about the fish!"

Yesterday, Today, Tomorrow

Tomorrow will be Althea and Monroe's wedding anniversary. Monroe smiled when he thought about it. When they were married all those years ago, they had no money for a honeymoon. They both had to work the next day. Every year, on their anniversary, Monroe and Althea talked about going on a trip. But something always happened. They could never get away.

Monroe looked over at Althea. She was sitting very still and looking out the window. He thought about their life together. Monroe really wanted to give his wife the honeymoon she always dreamed of. "What are you thinking?" Monroe asked her.

"I'm thinking about how time flies," she sighed. "It seems like only yesterday that you and I were just about to get married."

"Yesterday?" Monroe asked. "It sure seems like a long time ago to me. We were just kids. So many things have happened since that day."

Althea laughed. "A lot has changed. You're right. But I am very happy," she said. "Have these years been happy for you?"

"I could make a long list of all the things that have made me happy," Monroe said softly. "But this time 12 years ago, I was scared!"

"I was, too," Althea said, nodding.

Monroe said, "Well, now we can finally have our honeymoon. Wasn't it nice of Olga to offer to take care of Jody?"

"They are both very excited about it," said Althea. "I can't believe Jody is already 10 years old! It seems like only yesterday that she was a baby."

"You and your yesterdays," Monroe said. "I enjoyed every year of her life. But they were *years*, not *days!* To me, it seems like a long time since Jody was a baby."

"It makes me feel old when I think about how long ago she was born," Althea said. She shook her head and looked over at Monroe. "Do you feel old?"

"Sometimes," answered Monroe. "Do you remember when we had no money? We lived in that tiny apartment over the Chinese restaurant. I was making minimum wage."

"Yes—we were expecting Jody," said Althea. "And I was cleaning houses for extra money. But I was so happy. I felt like a queen."

"And then you got your GED," Monroe said. "You studied at night, even while you nursed the baby." Monroe patted the couch, and Althea came over and settled down beside him.

"I was so proud of you. I wanted to take you on a honeymoon then. But, with the baby we had no time."

"Or money," said Althea. "Do you remember when Jody broke her arm? It was two days before our seventh anniversary. We rushed her to the hospital. I was so scared! That put an end to our travel plans."

"I remember that I was mad at myself for giving her that bicycle," said Monroe.

"You couldn't protect her forever, Monroe," said Althea. "And she was tough. She was proud of her cast."

Althea leaned against Monroe. "And, because we stayed in town, you found out about the job at Seacoast Industries. I was proud of you when you were chosen. You have done very well there. They really like you."

"We got to move to a nicer place," Monroe said. "And we had more money. But we still didn't have our honeymoon. We were both working, and we couldn't get away."

"I know," Althea said. "Time and money. They both go so fast. And we never have enough of either." She and Monroe chuckled. "But I'm glad we moved here," Althea said. "We have such nice neighbors. This is a safe, happy place for Jody."

"She is growing up too fast," Monroe said. "I still think of her as my little girl." He shook his head. "She is getting so tall. And she has all these grown-up ideas. I wish I could slow down time."

"Time again," said Althea. "It rushes by so fast."

"We are going to slow down this weekend," said Monroe. "When we get up to the lake, we are going to just take it easy. We are going to relax and have a real honeymoon. Even if it is a few years late!"

Jody came into the room. "Mom," she said. "My throat hurts. I don't feel good."

Althea and Monroe looked at each other. Then they started to laugh. "It looks like we are going to have to wait another year before we have our honeymoon," he said.

Althea said, "That's OK. We've waited this long. Another year will just mean we have more memories to celebrate."